Big Barry Baker
and the bullies

Written by Gill and Paul Hamlyn
Illustrated by Philippe Dupasquier

Chapter 1

Big Barry Baker and his three friends,
Josie, Liz and Roy, were on their way
to school. Big Barry Baker started to run.
'Bet you can't catch me,' he shouted
as he ran off. Big Barry Baker always
liked to get to school first.
'We'll never catch him,' said Josie.
'Let's just walk.'

Just then, Josie, Liz and Roy heard
someone shouting and making a lot
of noise behind them.
They looked round and saw some
older children following them.
'We'll get you!' the older children
shouted.

The older children chased Josie, Liz and
Roy down the street.

'We're going to get you,' they shouted.
They could run much faster than
Josie, Liz and Roy and they quickly
came up behind them. Then, when no one
was looking, they pulled Josie down,
pushed Liz over and shouted at Roy.

When Josie, Liz and Roy got to school,
Big Barry Baker could see that they
were unhappy.

'Are you cross with me for running off?'
Barry called out.

'No,' said Liz, trying not to cry.

'What's the matter?' asked Barry.

'Nothing,' said Josie, looking at the cut
on her knee.

Big Barry Baker went over to his friends. 'If nothing is the matter, why do you look so unhappy?' he asked.

Josie, Liz and Roy looked at one another. 'Oh, go on,' said Josie, 'tell him.'

So Roy told Big Barry Baker all about how the older children had chased them and pushed them around.

'I'll get them next time,' said Roy.
'They won't bully me again!'
'Don't be stupid,' said Barry. 'They are
older than you so you might get hurt.
No, if you see them again, tell them
this - if they don't leave you alone, your
friend Big Barry Baker will come and
get them.'

After school, Big Barry Baker walked home with his friends. But Josie, Liz and Roy could not forget about the bullies. Every time they heard a noise they jumped and looked around. Big Barry Baker didn't like to see his friends so unhappy. 'I know,' he said. 'We could all go swimming. That will help us to forget about those bullies.'

Chapter 2

The next day Josie, Liz and Roy met
Big Barry Baker at the bus stop.
'My mum said I can go on my bike,'
said Barry, 'so I'll see you at the
swimming pool.' And off he went.
Soon the bus pulled up and Josie, Liz
and Roy got on. But they didn't see
the bullies sitting at the back of the bus.

'Look who it is,' said one of the bullies, and they started to move up the bus. One of them pulled Liz's pony-tail as hard as she could.

'Ouch!' said Liz. 'That hurt.'

But the bullies just laughed.

'Come on,' said Roy. 'They're just being stupid. Let's move.'

As Roy got up, another of the bullies came over and gave him a push.

'Stop that!' said the bus driver.

'Come on,' said Josie. 'This is our stop.'
The three friends jumped off the bus
as quickly as they could.
'Next time our friend Big Barry Baker
will get you,' Liz shouted to the bullies.
Josie started to cry. 'I'm scared,'
she said. 'What if we see them again on
the way home?'
Roy said, 'Let's go and find Barry.
He'll know what to do.'

By the time they had put on their
swimming costumes Big Barry Baker
was in the swimming pool. He always
liked to be the first one in the water.
Josie, Liz and Roy swam over to him
and Josie told him all about the bullies
on the bus.

'I bet they would have left us alone if
you had been there,' said Liz.

'Don't worry,' said Barry. 'Next time
we'll get them, won't we Roy?'

And he smiled at his friend.

'Come on,' he said. 'I bet I can swim
faster than you.'

When they came out of the swimming pool, Josie, Liz and Roy decided to walk home across the park with Barry.

'I hope we don't see those bullies again,' said Josie.

When they were in the park Barry said,
'Let's stop and play hide and seek.'
'I think we should just go home,' said Roy.
'Oh come on,' said Barry. 'Just one
quick game. Please! I'll hide and you
can all try to find me.'
Before they could say another word,
Big Barry Baker had gone.

'I'm scared,' said Josie.

'Come on then. Let's find Barry quickly
and go home,' said Roy.

So Josie, Liz and Roy began to look
for Barry.

They looked
behind the wall.

They looked
behind the big tree.

And they looked
by the swings.

Just then they saw some older children
coming across the park.

'Oh no,' said Liz. 'Look who it is!
Where's Barry when you need him?'

'We're not running away any more,'
said Roy.

As the bullies got nearer they started laughing and shouting, 'Where's this friend of yours then? Where's this Big Barry Baker?'

Suddenly they heard a shout.

'I'm Big Barry Baker! And these are my friends!'

Josie, Liz and Roy turned round.

There was Big Barry Baker. He had been hiding in the bushes right behind them.

The bullies stopped laughing.

They looked at Big Barry Baker.

He looked bigger than them - and he was very cross.

Now it was the bullies' turn to be scared.
They turned and ran back across the
park. Big Barry Baker ran after them.
'No one can run as fast as Big Barry
Baker,' shouted Josie, Liz and Roy
as loudly as they could.
They followed Big Barry Baker across
the park.

One of the bullies fell in the mud.

Another fell into a bush.

Then another tried
to jump over a wall
and hurt his knee.

One of them even
tried to climb
up a tree.

'They won't bully you any more,' said Big Barry Baker. 'Now they know it's not very nice being scared'.

'Thanks, Barry,' said Josie, Liz and Roy. The four friends walked off across the park. And this time they didn't look back. Not once!